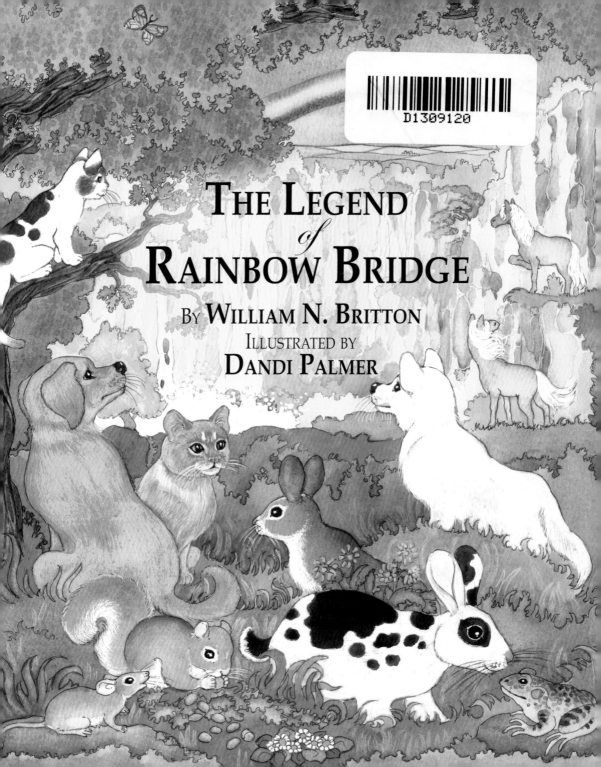

THE LEGEND
of
RAINBOW BRIDGE

BY WILLIAM N. BRITTON

ILLUSTRATED BY
DANDI PALMER

The Legend of Rainbow Bridge by William N. Britton
Illustrated by Dandi Palmer
Story copyright © 1994 William N. Britton
Illustrations copyright © 2007 Dandi Palmer
All rights reserved.

2011 Softcover Edition.
Published by Savannah Publishing.
Printed in China on recycled paper.

For information on quantity, wholesale or fundraising
purchases please contact Savannah Publishing at
SavannahPublishing.NET
LegendofRainbowBridge.com

A portion of the proceeds from this book go to animal-
rescue organizations dedicated to rescuing and caring
for abandoned and abused animals.

ISBN: 978-0-9764724-8-3

Until one has loved an animal,
a part of one's soul
remains unawakened.

~ Anatole France
(1844-1924)

About the Author

William N. Britton knows all about the therapeutic effect pets can have on a person. Bill, along with his wife Mickie, founded the Companion Golden Retriever Rescue (CGRR) in West Jordan, Utah. Together they rescued and "recycled" abandoned and abused Golden Retrievers. Since 1988, the CGRR has rescued thousands of dogs and found loving homes for all of them. Many of their dogs became companions to handicapped veterans. In his spare time, Bill writes stories and children's books about animals.

About the Illustrator

The beautiful illustrations in this book are the work of our extraordinary illustrator, Dandi Palmer. Dandi has been an illustrator for over thirty years. In addition to illustrating, she also writes adult science fiction novels under a pseudonym. Dandi resides in England and her wonderful illustrations have illuminated numerous children's books and adult publications. You can see more of her work at www.dandi.me.uk. Her main claim to absurdity is having grown a third set of teeth at the age of fourteen.

Dedication

On January 1, 2002, we lost a very special friend when Mickie (Vera) Britton was summoned to Rainbow Bridge. Even in our sorrow, we can't help but smile at the thought of the amazing welcome Mickie must have received when she arrived and was greeted by all the animals waiting there for her. Mickie was a kind, gentle and compassionate soul who knew how to dig in her heels and get things done. As founder of the Companion Golden Retriever Rescue in Utah, Mickie will forever be with us in spirit as those committed to animal rescue continue her work. Bless you, Mickie, you are an inspiration to us all.

This little book is dedicated to Mickie, to animal lovers everywhere, to anyone who has ever lost a beloved pet, and to all animals — those here on earth and those waiting for us in Rainbow Bridge.

THE LEGEND OF
RAINBOW BRIDGE

The Native American occupies a special place in the consciousness of all Americans. The lifestyle of the tribes and nations of Native Americans has been radically altered, both voluntarily and involuntarily, since the arrival of the White Man. The legends and stories, however, have a distinctive quality of life that still remains.

Quite a few children ask me questions about my love of nature, and especially my love and concern

for all dogs and the rest of God's creatures.

I found out very early in life that I don't have all the answers, but that I have more than my share of questions.

When I travel, I always have my dog Savannah with me. She is a big, 110-pound German Shepherd who loves all other animals and especially loves children. One day Savannah and I found ourselves visiting my friends in South Dakota at a Native American school for Sioux/Iroquois children. On the day of my visit, the children were learning about the closeness of family life.

Native American religion dominates all tribes and is at the very heart of their society. Every aspect of the tribe's life is

organized around it. Native American stories have a lesson to be learned by the listener, and very few of the stories change with the passage of time.

There was a Shaman who was visiting the school at the same time Savannah and I were there. A Shaman is a religious philosopher. He was telling the children about the importance of what the Native Americans called "The Sacred Circle."

I was so impressed by what he was saying that I had to take notes so I could pass his words on to others.

I know that most Native American storytellers rarely, if ever, relate the full legend. Only the storyteller is privileged to know the whole tale.

     With his back to the audience,
the Shaman put on his storytelling mask.
When he turned around, his mask revealed
the face of a man unsmiling.
     He began to speak. "For Native
American people of all nations, all power
comes from the Sacred Circle. So long as
the Circle remains unbroken, the people
will flourish.
     "The direction East gives us peace
and light. The direction South gives us
warmth. From the West, we are given
rain, and from the North, with its cold
and mighty winds, we are given strength
and endurance."
     I was quite moved by what the
Shaman was saying, and when he asked if

any of us had any questions of our own, I asked the Shaman, "Where does my dog go when he dies? Is this the end? Is it not true that my dog is part of my Sacred Circle?"

The Shaman said that he would tell us of a place called Rainbow Bridge. As he started his story, the boys and girls, and of course Savannah and I, crowded around his feet.

When he started to talk, I glanced around the room and saw that every window had someone leaning in to listen. Not a sound could be heard. Even the birds out in the sagebrush had stopped their singing.

I wished I were an artist and could paint a portrait of him in the center of that group of adults and children.

He began, "Just this side of
Heaven is a place called Rainbow
Bridge. When a pet dies who
has been especially close to a
person on earth, that pet goes to
Rainbow Bridge.

"There are beautiful
meadows and grassy hills there
for all our special friends so they
can run and play together. There
is always plenty of their favorite
food to eat, plenty of fresh spring

water for them to drink, and
every day is filled with sunshine so our
little friends are warm and comfortable.

"All the pets that had been ill or old
are now restored to health and youth. Those
that had been hurt or maimed are now whole
and strong again, just as we remember them
in our dreams of days gone by.

"The pets we loved are happy and content except for one small thing. Each one misses someone very special who was left behind.

"They all run and play together, but the day comes when one of them suddenly stops and looks off into the distant hills.

"It is as if he has heard a whistle or was given a signal of some kind. His eyes are bright and intent. His body begins to quiver.

"All at once he breaks away from the group, flying like a deer over the grass, his little legs carrying him faster and faster.

"You have been spotted, and when you and your special friend finally meet, you hug and cling to him in joyous reunion, never to be parted again.

"Happy kisses rain upon your face. Your hands once again caress the beloved head. You look once more into the trusting eyes of your pet so long gone from your life, but never gone from your heart.

"Then with your beloved pet by your side, you will cross the Rainbow Bridge together. Your Sacred Circle is now complete again."

The Shaman looked down. He was through telling the tale. I gave Savannah a tight hug around her neck. And she, well, she looked up at me and licked a tear from my cheek.

In Loving Memory of

*who graced our lives
and filled our hearts
with unconditional love.*

For information on quantity, wholesale or fundraising purchases
please contact Savannah Publishing at
SavannahPublishing.NET
LegendofRainbowBridge.com

A portion of the proceeds from this book goes to
animal rescue organizations dedicated to rescuing and caring
for abandoned and abused animals.

*Love the animals,
Love the plants,
Love everything.
If you love everything, you will
 perceive the divine mystery in things.
Once you perceive it, you will begin to
 comprehend it better every day.
And you will come at last to love the
whole world with an all-embracing love.*
—Fyodor Dostoevsky
(1821–1881)